"I'D LIKE TO DEDICATE THIS BOOK TO MY EVER-PRESENT HELP, DAVINA, WHO CONTINUES TO LOVE AND SUPPORT ME THROUGH ALL THE CRAZINESS, AND TO THE NEWDAY TEAM - DEAR FRIENDS AND BROTHERS-IN-ARMS WHO HAVE TRUSTED MY CRAZY HUNCHES WHEN MANY WOULDN'T." STEFAN

"I'D LIKE TO DEDICATE MY PART IN THIS BOOK TO MY WIFE, ALI, WHO ORIGINALLY THOUGHT I WAS HEADED FOR A NICE, STABLE JOB IN THE LEGAL PROFESSION. THANK YOU FOR YOUR LOVE, ENCOURAGEMENT, FAITH AND SUPPORT." DAN

First published in 2016 by Liston and Jones

Text © Stefan Liston 2015
Illustrations © Dan Jones 2016

Printed in the United Kingdom by Swallowtail Print

ISBN 978-0-9956198-0-7

The rights of Stefan Liston to be identified as the author and Dan Jones to be identified as the illustrator have been asserted by them in accordance with the Copyright, Design and Patents Act 1988

Typography: White Wood, Bebas Neue and Arial

A CIP catalogue record for this book is available from the British Library

For news and future projects, or to get in touch, visit:
www.anchor-lines.com/book

WE WOULD ALSO LIKE TO SAY A HUGE AND HEARTFELT THANK YOU TO ALL THOSE WHOSE CONTRIBUTIONS THROUGH PRAYER, ENCOURAGEMENT AND PRE-ORDERS HAVE MADE THIS BOOK POSSIBLE. THANK YOU!

HI THERE, MY NAME'S STEFAN AND I LIVE WITH DAVINA, DAISY, LEVI AND MELODY IN THE LONDON BOROUGH OF CAMDEN, WHERE I'M A VERY HAPPY MEMBER AND PASTOR OF REVELATION CHURCH, LONDON. YOU CAN FIND OUT MORE AT:

WWW.REVELATIONCHURCH.ORG.UK

I LOVE FAMILY TIME, READING TIME, THINKING TIME AND PRAYING TIME. I LOVE LONDON. I ALSO LOVE THE SEA. I ALSO REALLY LOVE CUSTARD CREAMS.

I'M DAN AND I LIVE WITH MY WIFE ALI AND OUR TWO KIDS, ANNABELLE AND LUKE IN NORWICH WHERE WE'RE PART OF KING'S COMMUNITY CHURCH NORWICH. WHEN I'M NOT CHANGING NAPPIES I SPEND MY TIME WORKING AS AN ILLUSTRATOR DRAWING LOTS AND LOTS OF PICTURES. IF YOU'D LIKE TO SEE MORE OF MY WORK, YOU CAN FIND ME ONLINE AT:

WWW.ANCHOR-LINES.COM

WE HOPE YOU ENJOY THE BOOK

HE WAS AND IS AND IS TO COME

BEFORE AIR

OR LIGHT

**OR SPINNING
SPHERES**

BEFORE DEPTHS
AND MYSTERIES

AND FIRST WINGED FLIGHTS

BEFORE ANYTHING THAT WE NOW SEE,

AND LOVE OR LONG FOR, OR WANT TO BE

BEFORE ALL THE DREAMING
AND INVENTIONS

BEFORE ALL THE SCHEMING
AND CONVENTIONS

BEFORE ALL THE CULTURES
AND THE NATIONS

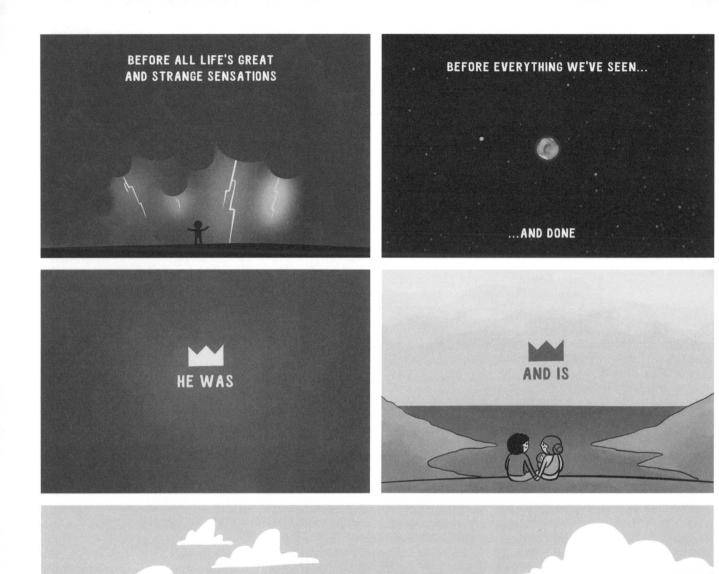

BEFORE THE **THOUGHT** OF YOU WERE HERE

BEFORE THE FIRST AND GREAT IDEA

BEFORE ALL EMPIRES GRAND WITH GLORY

efore the first line of any story

BEFORE THE RISING OF OUR SUN

AND SETTING WHEN ITS WORK IS DONE

BEFORE THE ANCIENT WORKS WERE STARTED

BEFORE THE SEA AND LAND WERE PARTED

BEFORE THE BUZZING OF THE CREATURES

BEFORE THE POINTS THE COMPASS REACHES

BEFORE THE SKIES WERE FILLED WITH WATERS

BEFORE THE JOY OF SONS

AND DAUGHTERS

BEFORE THE KISSES OF TRUE LOVERS

BEFORE THE NURTURE OF GOOD MOTHERS

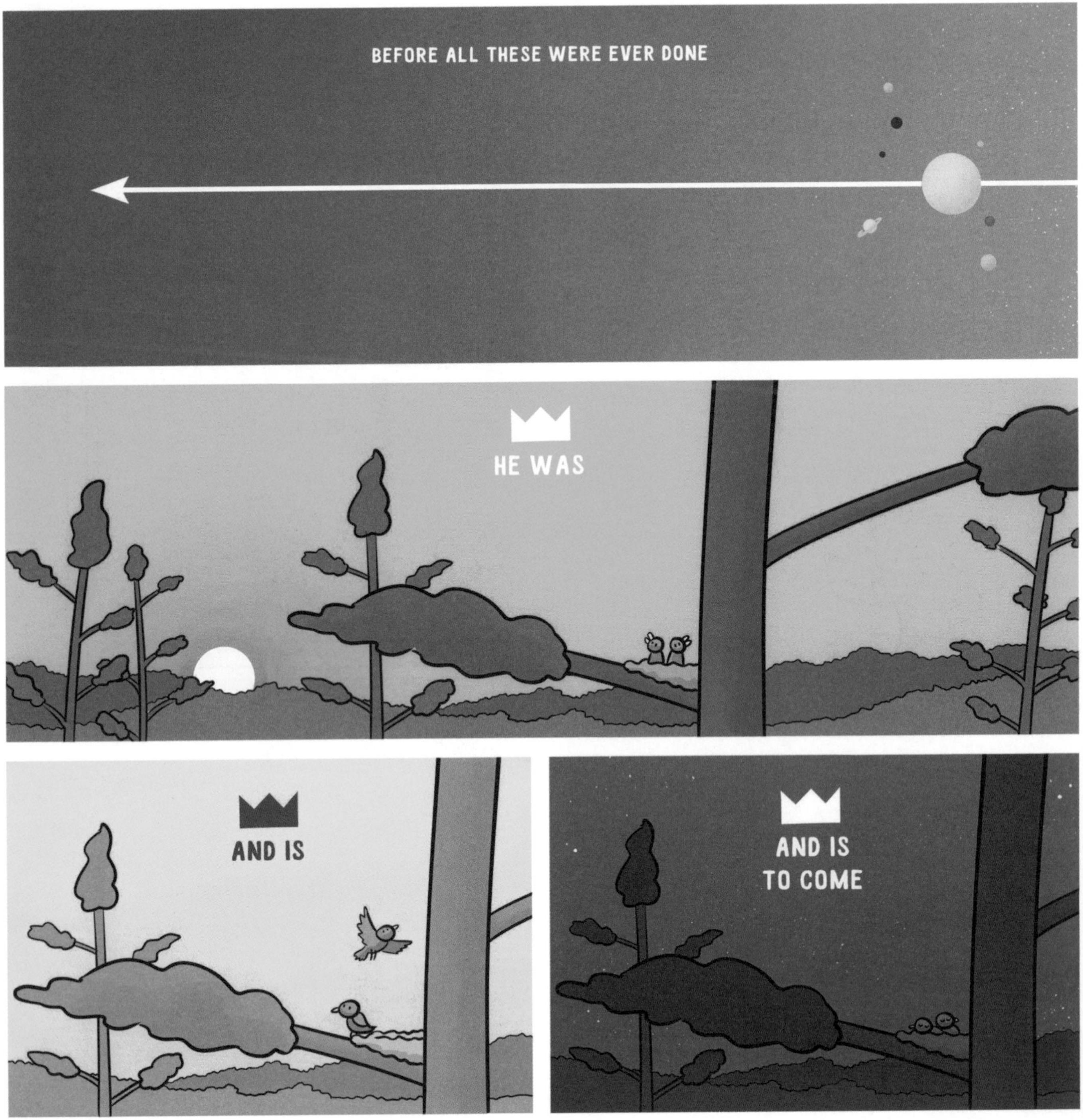
BEFORE ALL THESE WERE EVER DONE
HE WAS
AND IS
AND IS
TO COME

BEFORE ALL THINGS THIS
ONE
AND
THREE

WITH HEART OF LOVE

AND WILL SO FREE

WITH SOVEREIGN POWER AND TENDER PASSION

STOOD ALONE AND WISELY FASHIONED

EARTH'S FOUNDATIONS IN PERFECTION

MIGHTY WISDOM

KEEN SELECTION

LET THERE BE LIGHT

PERFECT WORDS PERFECTLY SPOKEN

HE SMASHED IT

AS THE DAWN WAS BROKEN

BIRDS

AND BEASTS

AND SWIMMING CREATURES

VALLEYS...

...FORESTS...

STUNNING FEATURES

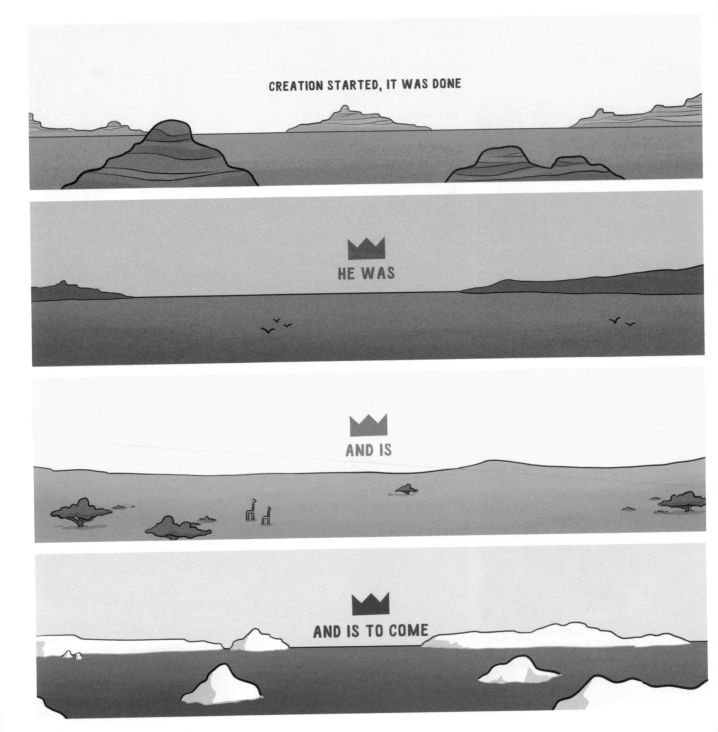

BEFORE YOUR FIRST AND *GASPING* BREATH

YOUR TINY LITTLE LIFE AND DEATH

YOU ARE HERE

YOUR TRIUMPHS AND YOUR DEAREST TREASURES

YOUR COSIEST AND NEAREST PLEASURES

YOUR FAILINGS...

...AND YOUR AWKWARD STUMBLINGS

YOUR MIGHTY SPEECHES

AND SHAMEFUL MUMBLINGS

YOUR CHOICES MADE IN FOOLISH ERROR

THE MOMENTS OF YOUR PUREST TERROR

THE THINGS IN LIFE THAT MEAN SO MUCH

THOSE THINGS THAT SEEM SO DEAR TO TOUCH

THE THINGS THAT MEAN SO MUCH I SAID

SO MUCH TO YOU

IN HEART AND HEAD

BEFORE YOUR TINY LIFE AND DEATH

THIS TIME OF YOURS

THIS WISPY BREATH

only a small bag of stones was found.

if he'd known they would be his last words he might perhaps have chosen something a little less political—

ALL OF YOUR YEARS AND WHAT THEY SUM

Countess Lydia Thorpe
1922 - 2016

Her ladyship died this week in a hunting accident after a tragic mishap involving a loaded shotgun and a rogue badger. A legendary socialite and wit, she will be sorely missed for her contributions to both charity and fashion. She leaves behind four children and eight grandchildren, along with a highly prized estate in Kent.

Franklin Powers
1939 - 2016

Forename Surname
1952 - 2016

Forename Surname passed away this week in his sleep. Respected in his local community, he was widowed at 30 and never remarried. He leaves behind a dog, Barkus Aurelius.

He will be buried alongside his wife next week.

Mr Big
1973 - 2016

Mr Big has been a fixture of the competitive eating scene since local tournaments first began in '84. He is well known for achieving Olympic silver in the burrito category and for a long-standing rivalry with Dutchman Henrick Largemann. He leaves behind a vast pantry and training facility to be used for up and coming underprivileged eaters.

Dr. Lars Ludwig
1948 - 2016

Lars, noted eccentric and famed inventor, perished

HE WAS   AND IS   AND IS TO COME

PAUSE

IT'S TIME FOR DEEP REFLECTION

BEFORE THE NIGHT
OF YOUR CONCEPTION

WHEN SEED AND EGG
COMBINED TO MAKE YOU

WHEN BODIES ENTWINED
DID CREATE YOU

WHETHER IT WAS LOVE OR LUST

VIOLENCE OR TENDER TRUST

WHETHER IT WAS KIND AND CARING

OR INNOCENCE DESTROYED "NOT FAIR!" IN
ANY WAY YOU WERE CONCEIVED

THE EYES OF HIM WHO ALWAYS SEES

THE HEART OF HIM WHO ALWAYS KNOWS

THE LOVE OF HIM THAT ALWAYS FLOWS

THE PLAN OF HIM WHO HAS ALL SIGHT

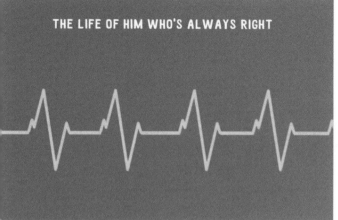

THE LIFE OF HIM WHO'S ALWAYS RIGHT

THE STAMP OF HIM WHO HAS ALL GLORY

WAS PRESSED ON **YOU** SO THAT YOUR STORY

COULD BE WRITTEN WITH PURE GOLD

COULD BE BROUGHT IN FROM THE COLD

WHO WAS

AND IS

AND IS TO COME

HE **TOWERS** OVER HIS CREATION

HE FACES DOWN
THE PROUD AND HIGH

HE LISTENS FOR
THE DESPERATE CRY

HE
KEEPS
HIS
PROMISES
FOREVER

HE *DOES NOT LEAVE*
IN STORMY WEATHER

NO ONE
ELSE COMES
CLOSE
TO THIS

HE'S

BETTER!

THAN YOUR
GREATEST
WISH

ALL THESE THINGS

AND MORE!

HE'S DONE

WHO WAS

AND IS

AND IS
TO COME

AND IF IT COULDN'T GET MUCH STRANGER

HE COMES TO US INSIDE A MANGER?

GET YOUR HEAD
AROUND
THAT MOMENT

IT'S MORE THAN
JUST A
BIZARRE OMEN

IT WAS PLANNED TO HELP US SEE

THAT HIS WAYS AND OURS THEY DON'T AGREE

THINGS WE THINK ARE SO DARN GREAT

THINGS THAT MAKE US **SHOUT** OR *QUAKE*

HE LOOKS ON JUST UNIMPRESSED

HE LOOKS ON WITH DISINTEREST

SHEPHERDS WERE THE FIRST TO KNOW

SHEPHERDS! PEOPLE THOUGHT OF LOW!

ANGELS, GLORY, SONGS, NO JOKE

THIS IS THE WAY OF THE HOLY ONE

WHO WAS

AND IS
TO COME

AND IS

HE'S THE KING OF HEARTS,
THE BROKEN-HEARTED

THE MAN OF SORROWS,
WHO WON'T BE PARTED

FROM HIS CHURCH

THE BRIDE HE TREASURES

FROM WHOM HIS HEART ENJOYS SUCH PLEASURES

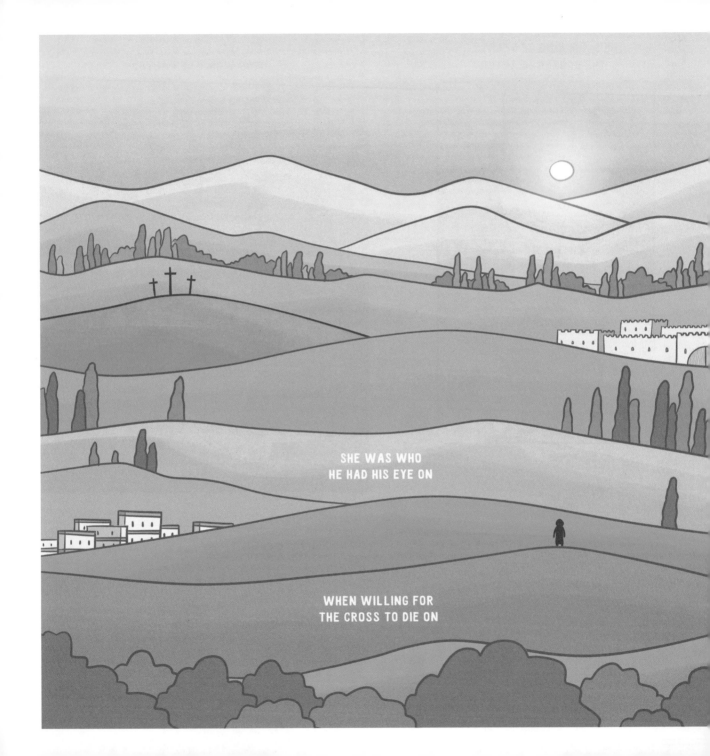

SHE WAS BURNING IN HIS HEART

AS NAILS AND WHIPS TORE HIM APART

SHE WAS THE GOAL HE WAS PURSUING

AS HE EMBRACED NEAR TOTAL RUIN

FOR HER HE FULLY POURED HIS LIFE OUT

FOR HER HE WEPT
AND BLED
AND CRIED OUT

"TODAY MY FRIEND   *WE'LL BE IN GLORY*"

"WHEN ALL THIS MADNESS QUIETENS DOWN
I'M WRITING YOU INTO THE STORY"

"THEY'LL HEAR OF YOU
FROM TOWN TO TOWN"

"FROM THIS POINT ON"

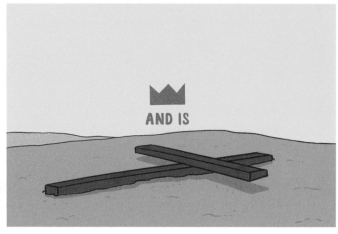

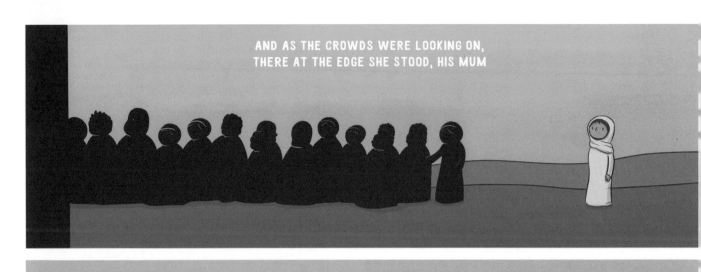

AND AS THE CROWDS WERE LOOKING ON,
THERE AT THE EDGE SHE STOOD, HIS MUM

THIS BLESSED LADY NOW CAUGHT UP IN
MIGHTY THINGS THERE WAS NO STOPPING

BUT JESUS HANGING SAW HER FACE

HIS MOTHER'S FACE

HIS MOTHER'S FACE

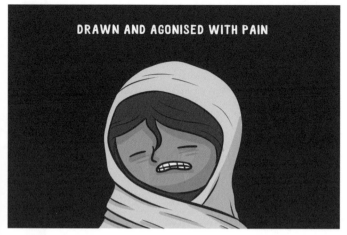

DRAWN AND AGONISED WITH PAIN

WITHOUT HIM HOW WOULD SHE LIVE AGAIN?

HE CALLED TO JOHN "YOU SEE MY MOTHER?
RIGHT NOW SHE NEEDS HER SON, MY BROTHER"

"RIGHT NOW SHE NEEDS TO BE ADOPTED"

"AND YOU'RE THE GUY, FOR YOU I'VE OPTED"

AND AS THE SKY WAS
DARK WITH BLACKNESS

AND AS HIS BODY
HUNG IN SLACKNESS

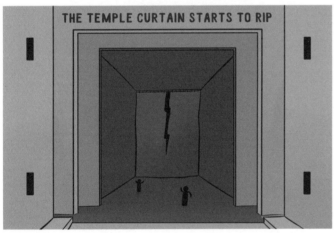

THE TEMPLE CURTAIN STARTS TO RIP

THE DARKNESS KINGDOM STARTS TO FLIP

THE ANCIENT SERPENT FEELS THE BRUISING

ON HIS HEAD BY JESUS' WOUNDING

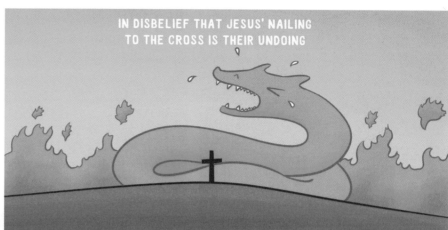

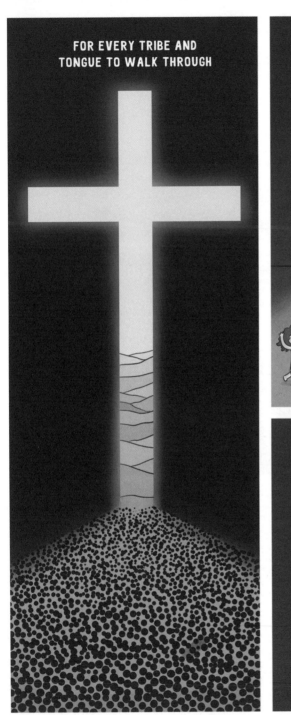

AS JESUS LIFTED UP A CRY

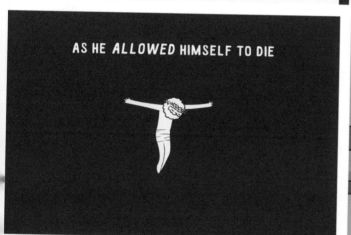

AS HE *ALLOWED* HIMSELF TO DIE

HE CRIED OUT   "MY JOB IS DONE"

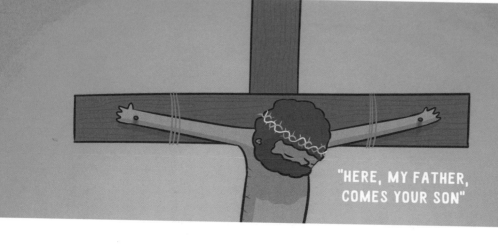

"HERE, MY FATHER, COMES YOUR SON"

WHAT CAME NEXT
WAS VERY QUIET

IF YOU DIDN'T KNOW...
YOU'D JUST PASS BY IT

JESUS LAID BEHIND A ROCK

DISAPPOINTMENT, FIT TO DROP

TIRED, EXHAUSTED THOSE WHO'D FOLLOWED

HOPES AND DREAMS TURNED OUT SO HOLLOW

WHAT COULD THERE BE NOW FOR THEM
BUT BITTER MEMORIES END TO END?

NOSTALGIA MAYBE, NOTHING MORE

UNDERLINING JUST HOW POOR

THEY WERE WITHOUT HIM GONE THEIR MASTER

MAY LIFE FLY AWAY JUST FASTER

THERE'S NOTHING NOW WORTH LIVING FOR

IN HIS EYES THEY HAD SEEN MORE

THE MORE THEIR SOULS THEY KNEW WERE MADE FOR

THE MORE THEIR DEEPEST DEPTHS THEY CRAVED FOR

IN HIS EYES THEY'D SEEN IT THERE

IN HIS EYES THEY'D *DREAMED* AND *DARED*...

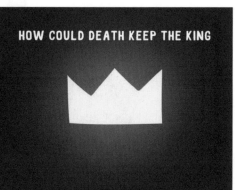

HOW COULD DEATH KEEP THE KING

THE SON

THE WORD OF LIFE

FROM WALKING FREELY
FROM ITS GRASP?

THIS THING WAS *EASY*

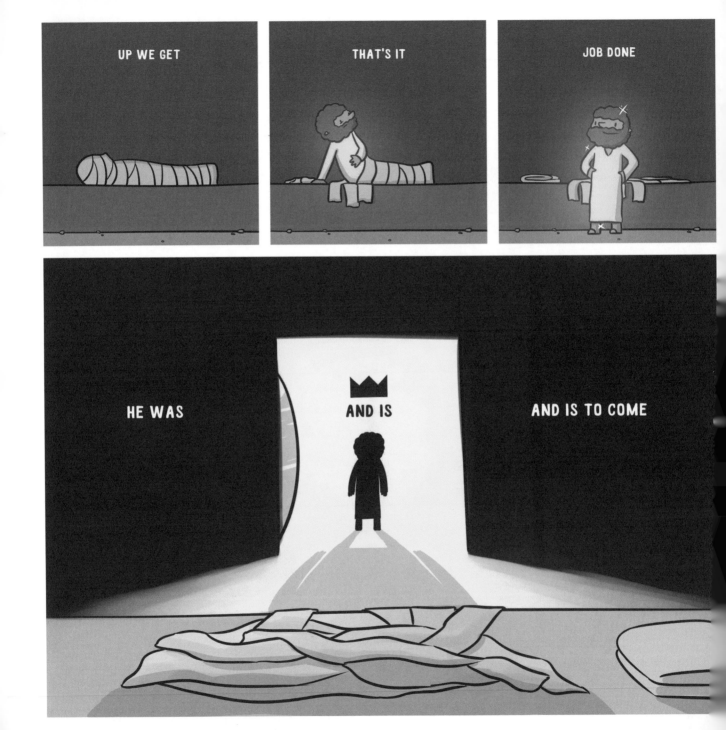

AFTER 40 DAYS OF VISITS

OF CAUSING FOLKS TO THINK "HMM..."

"IS IT?"

AFTER PROVING BEYOND DOUBT,
YES IT IS YOU'RE FREE TO SHOUT

AND SING AND DANCE IT'S REALLY ME

YES DANCE AND SING YOU'RE NOW SET FREE

TO TELL THE WORLD YOUR SAVIOUR'S LIVING

THE CROSS, IT REALLY WAS ME GIVING

HOPE AND LIFE TO ALL WHO TRUST

TRUTH AND PEACE - YES, THESE THINGS MUST BE SHOUTED OUT IN EVERY NATION

THE GLAD TIDINGS OF SALVATION

AFTER THESE GREAT 40 DAYS
THERE CAME THE MOMENT TO PART WAYS

JERUSALEM HEAVEN SAMARIA

BUT NOT BEFORE HE MADE THE VOW
I'M WITH YOU HERE

AND WITH YOU NOW

BUT ALSO WITH YOU WHEN I GO
ALSO WITH YOU TOMORROW

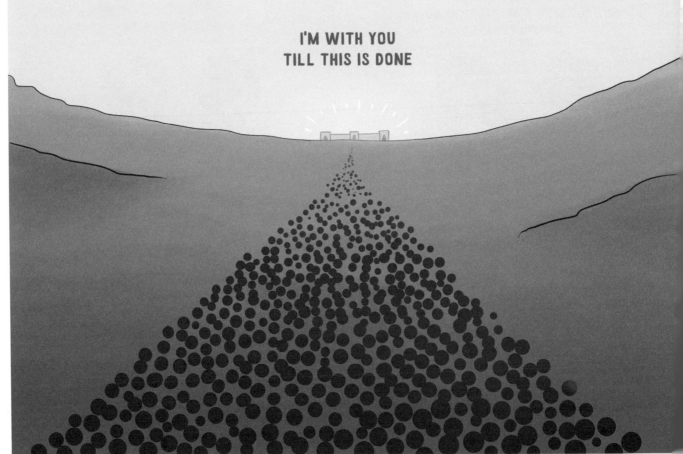

SO COMFORT, COMFORT ONE AND ALL

COMFORT TO THE GREAT...

...AND SMALL

COMFORT FROM THE KING OF GLORY

COMFORT IN YOUR MESSY STORY

COMFORT FROM THE ROCK OF AGES

COMFORT WHEN THE BATTLE RAGES

COMFORT FROM THE LORD OF WONDER

COMFORT FROM HIS VOICE OF THUNDER

AND HEALING IN YOUR WOUNDS AND FAILINGS HEALING IN YOUR CRIES AND WAILINGS

HEALING IN YOUR SILENT MUSINGS

HEALING FOR YOUR FOOLISH CHOOSINGS

HEALING BY THE LORD YOUR HEALER

HEALING FROM ALL
THE WICKED STEALER

HAS TRIED TO RUB INTO YOUR PAIN

AND TRIED TO MAKE YOU LIVE AGAIN

AND TRIED TO KILL
YOU BY REPEATING

LIES

ON LIES

ON LIES

SO EATING
YOU UP FROM THE INSIDE

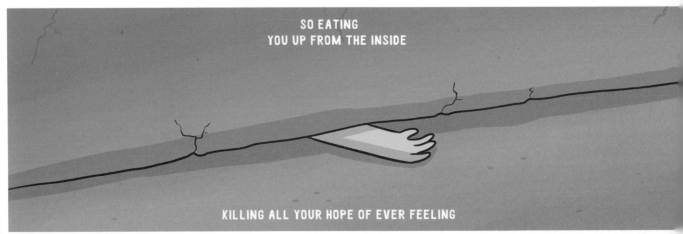

KILLING ALL YOUR HOPE OF EVER FEELING

HIS FORGIVENESS AND HIS LIGHTNESS

HIS REDEMPTION AND HIS BRIGHTNESS

HEALING NOW TO YOU MY FRIEND
HEALING FROM THE KING WHO'LL SEND

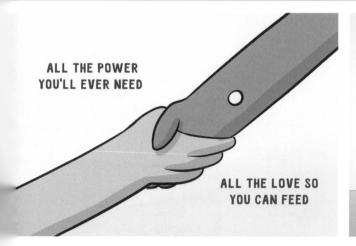

ALL THE POWER
YOU'LL EVER NEED

ALL THE LOVE SO
YOU CAN FEED

ON ALL THE GOOD STUFF FROM HIS THRONE

YOU'RE WELCOMED IN,
YOU'RE WELCOMED HOME

HEALING FLOWS FROM
GOD'S GOOD SON

WHO WAS

AND IS

AND IS
TO COME

AND AS WE PONDER WHAT WILL HAPPEN
TOMORROW AND THEN THROUGH THE YEARS

WE REALISE THERE IS NO MAP

AND THERE'S SO MUCH BOTH FAR AND NEAR

SO MUCH OVER THE HORIZON

SO MUCH THAT WE JUST DON'T KNOW

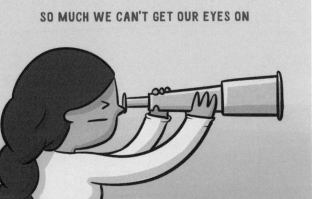

SO MUCH WE CAN'T GET OUR EYES ON

SO MUCH THAT OUR MINDS COULD BLOW

BUT THERE IS ONE THING WE CAN SETTLE

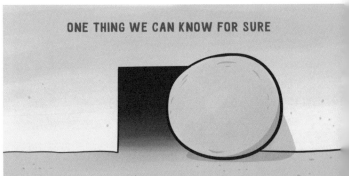

ONE THING WE CAN KNOW FOR SURE

HE'S ABOVE IT

HE IS WITH US

WE CAN TRUST HIM

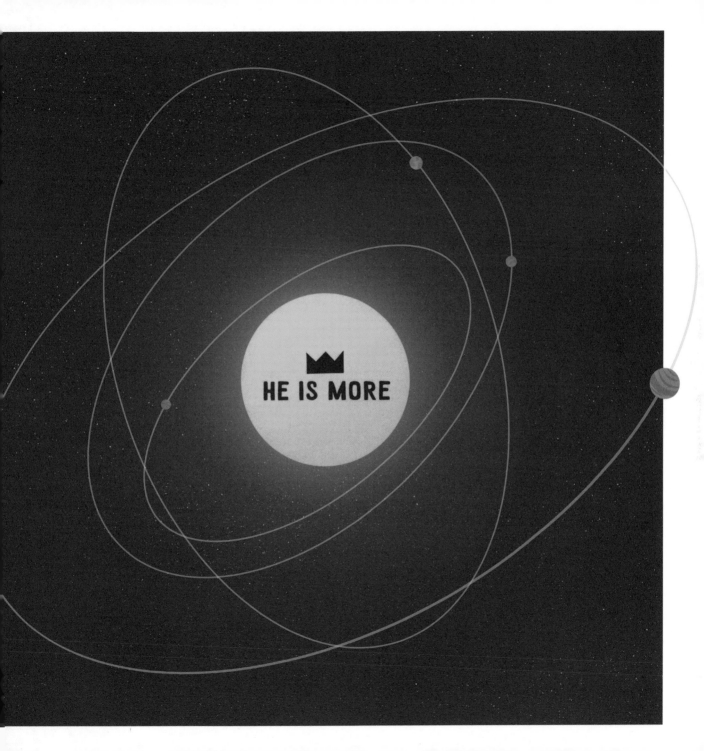

HE WILL COME
AGAIN IN POWER

HE WILL RAISE US
FROM THE DEAD

EVERY EYE WILL SEE HIS SPLENDOUR

"FAITHFUL ARE THESE WORDS" HE SAID

SO WE CAN REST OUR WEIGHT UPON THEM

WE CAN GIVE OUR LIVES FOR THIS

WE CAN DAILY OFFER UP THE PAIN, THE MESS

THE JOY, THE BLISS

'COS WE'RE THE ONES BEEN FOUND BY JESUS

WE'VE BEEN CHOSEN BY THE SON

YES, WE ARE IN *AWE* OF HIM

WHO WAS

AND IS...

...TO COME...